OXFORD*Playscripts*

●●●●●●●●●●●●●●●●●●●●●●●●●●●●●●●●●●

Series Editor – Bill Lucas

Kelvin Reynolds

the *T*een *C*ommandments

Oxford University Press   1992

Oxford University Press, Walton Street, Oxford OX2 6DP

Oxford New York Toronto
Delhi Bombay Calcutta Madras Karachi
Kuala Lumpur Singapore Hong Kong Tokyo
Nairobi Dar es Salaam Cape Town
Melbourne Auckland Madrid

and associate companies in
Berlin Ibadan

Oxford is a trade mark of Oxford University Press

ISBN 0 19 831275 X

Typeset by Pentacor PLC High Wycombe, Bucks

Printed and bound in Great Britain at the University Press, Cambridge

A CIP catalogue record for this book is available from the British
Library

Contents

The Locations

Scene

1	Corridor	int. day
2	Dining room/common room	int. day
3	Path/farm track	ext. day
4	Path/farm track near to hedge	ext. day
5	Apartment	int. day
6	Apartment	int. evening
7	Playground	ext. day
8	Dining room/common room	int. day
9	Greenspace committee room	int. day
10	Classroom	int. day
11	Apartment	int. day
12	Playground	ext. day
13	Greenspace committee room	int. day
14	Playground	ext. day
15	Blackberry Way	ext. day
16	Greenspace committee room	int. day
17	Corridor	int. day
18	Dining room/common room	int. day

The Characters

Ben Turner	*In love with Melissa Curran.*
Kyle	*Ben's friend.*
Jack	*Another friend.*
Lavinia Holdsworth	*Chairperson of Greenspace.*
April	*Lavinia's friend, and a member of Greenspace.*
Rosie Turner	*Ben's mother.*
Kelly	*Ben's sister.*
Giles Fortescue	*Rosie's boyfriend, an all-round entrepreneur.*
Melissa Curran	*Ben's idol. A member of Greenspace. (Non-speaking part.)*
Carol	*A friend of Melissa's.*
Grace	*A member of Greenspace.*
First child **Second child** }	*Playing on Blackberry Way.*
Greenspace girl	*At Blackberry Way demonstration.*
Mr Taylor	*A Council official.*

NO PLACE FOR TOXIC WASTE GREENPEACE

TOXIC WASTE

DO NOT HANDLE

England and Wales produce an estimated 480 million tonnes of waste a year, plus millions of tonnes of liquid industrial waste and sewage. They also import over 40,000 tonnes of hazardous waste every year, from other countries unwilling or unable to deal with it themselves.

1 *Corridor* *int. day*

    a *Close up of young girl's face. She screams loudly.*

    Cut to

    b *Boy's face – showing shock and bewilderment. Camera pulls back, boy is holding what appears to be a knife or surgical instrument in hand. (No dialogue – separate shots.)*

    c *Moving sequences – camera follows tiny drops of blood down a corridor – swift pace, no dialogue – no person seen in shot – theme music played.*

. . . .

2 *Dining room / common room* *int. day*

(Camera pans several tables, then close up of one table. Three boys seated – one boy with head in hands)

Ben:
What have I done? What have I done? Melissa Curran, that vision of loveliness, that. . . that crystal jewel set in a silver crown. . .

Jack:
Or something like that!

Ben: *(looking up, grabs **Jack**'s arm)*
What have I done to her?

Kyle:
Bit OTT my son.

Ben:
She'll never speak to me again.

Kyle:
She didn't speak to you before.

Ben:
I could have killed her. One slip of the scalpel, I could have killed her.

Kyle:
Come off it. You only nicked the top of Melissa's finger, you haven't amputated her arm.

Ben:
She could die of blood poisoning.

Kyle: *(groaning)*
Look, she's fine. I saw her in the medical room ten minutes ago. A little drop of iodine and a minute elastoplast. That's all. Not major surgery.

Ben:
She blames me, I know she blames me.

Kyle:
Of course she does. You did it.

Jack:
How did it happen?

Ben:
I only wanted to help. We were cutting up onions in biology. I could see Melissa was having trouble, so I went across and said I'd cut the onion for her.

*(**Jack** and **Kyle** laugh)*

Ben: *(demonstrates with pencil)*
It was our first time in the new science set. I suppose I was nervous, just standing there next to Melissa, the knife just slipped – will she be OK, Kyle?

Kyle:
Of course she will.

Jack: *(puts arm round **Ben** in sombre mood. Mock American accent)* Ben, she's gonna be all right!

*(All laugh except for **Ben** who looks miserable)*

· ·

3 Path/farm track   ext. day

*(Rural or park setting. **Kyle** and **Ben** walking down path discussing events)*

Kyle:
You could go and apologize.

Ben:
Apologize! It's taken me six months to pluck up courage to speak to her. The best looking girl in the school and I've blown it.

*(**Ben** looks skywards)*

Kyle:
Just be cool, man. Be cool. Hey look.

*(**Kyle** nods in distance)*

Ben:
What?

Kyle:
Lavinia Holdsworth! Over there. What's she doing? Come on, let's have some fun.

· ·

4 Path/farm track near to hedge   ext. day

*(**Lavinia** and **April** crouched on ground examine jars, taking notes with clipboards. **Kyle** creeps behind **Lavinia**, puts hands over her eyes and begins mumbling in 'David Bellamy' voice)*

Kyle:
Here we have a wemarkable specimen, the lesser spotted Lavinia Holdsworth, a most weliable, wivetting creature whose –

*(**Lavinia** turns, grabs **Kyle**'s arm and twists, pulling him to the ground)*

Kyle: *(scrambles to feet yelling)*
Ouch! Watch it. You could have broken my arm.

Lavinia: *(smiling sweetly)*
Next time I'll make certain.

Kyle:
That's the trouble with you lot. No sense of humour.

April: *(looking up)*
This is a serious study, not that you'd understand.

Kyle: *(to **Ben**)*
Oh, serious study! And what species are we saving today?

Lavinia:
Well, it won't be you two, for a start.

April:
I heard that you're trying to wipe out members of the human race. Melissa Curran?

Kyle: *(pointing to **Ben**)*
That was him.

Lavinia:
Oh yes, how is the knifeman of Somerton High School? Still lacerating your way through Year Nine?

Ben:
Wasn't my fault. It was an accident.

April:
Look, we are rather busy. What do you want?

Kyle: *(picks up jar of water – camera close-up)*
Just curious. Urghh! Don't fancy your coffee, Lavinia. Get a whiff of this, Benny!

April: *(takes back jar)*
Actually it's a sample from the pond. We're measuring the effect of acid rain on the environment.

Kyle:
Ooo!

Lavinia:
Did you know that the world's most acid rain fell on Scotland in 1974? It was sourer than vinegar.

Kyle:
Fancy that. Vinegar rain. Handy for fish and chips.

April:
We'd expect a stupid remark like that from you.

Lavinia:
It's a waste of time explaining it to them. They have absolutely no conception of what we are trying to do.

Kyle:
So you think your ecobiological group Greengage or whatever it's called –

Lavinia:
Greenspace!

Kyle:
All right, Greenspace then, is going to change the world?

Lavinia: *(picking up notes)*
No. But at least *we* care what happens to our world.

Kyle:
And so do we. Don't we, Ben?

*(**Ben** picks up second jar containing black slug)*

Ben: *(peers into jar – close up)*
What's this?

Lavinia: *(sighs)*
Found in the gutters and drains, one of the lowest forms of life. A thick mass of blubber with nought-point-nought-five of a brain cell.

Ben:
Poor little slug! Don't talk about him like that.

Lavinia: *(snatching jar back)*
I was referring to you. By comparison the slug is infinitely more intelligent. Come on, April, we've got work to do.

*(**Lavinia** takes jars, collects notes / clipboard. She and **April** walk off)*

Ben:
Who needs acid rain with them around! I hate them two and their stupid club.

Kyle:
Listen, Melissa Curran belongs to Greenspace.

Ben:
So?

Kyle:
So? If you want to impress Melissa, join Greenspace. She might take you more seriously then.

Ben:
Oh, come off it. Join Greenspace! With those two running it? You must be joking. Besides, they won't let me in.

Kyle:
I bet you . . . eh. . . my new Iron Maiden album that you can't get in Greenspace!

Ben: *(ponders for a moment)*
All right, you're on. I'll ask them tomorrow.

*(**Kyle** and **Ben** slap hands in agreement)*

5   Apartment

*(Dining room. Opening shot of T-shirt thrown through the air. n_ **Kelly** sitting on chair reading magazine)*

Rosie:
You can clear this mess up for a start. We do have a washing basket round here, in case anyone hasn't noticed.

Kelly: *(irritated)*
Oh, Mum!

*(**Rosie** approaches **Ben** who is sitting at table with headphones on, oblivious to the shouting going on. **Rosie** slams open can of beans with fork on table in front of him. **Ben** takes headset off)*

Rosie:
And these are yours, I presume?

Ben:
I wondered what happened to them.

Rosie:
Get rid of them now! I am not your skivvy.

Ben: *(spoons beans into mouth)*
Don't give me hassle, Mum, I've had a bad day.

Rosie:
If you don't pull your weight round here, it will get even worse.

*(**Rosie** storms off into kitchen area)*

Ben: *(pushes beans aside)*
I'm going out.

Kelly:
No you're not. Giles Fortescue is coming to dinner. We've got to stay in, make polite conversation.

Ben:
Oh, no. Giles's not coming round tonight?

Kelly:
'Fraid so.

Ben:
Bore of the week.

*(**Ben** shouts to **Rosie**)*
Oi, Mum, do I have to stay in if Giles's coming round?

*(**Rosie** returns)*

Rosie:
Yes, Ben, you do. For once this family is going to sit round the dining table together. A very rare event these days. And I'll thank you not to refer to my friends in that way.

Kelly:
Friends? You fancy him something rotten.

Rosie:
Kelly, Giles is just a business friend, that's all. We have . . . a platonic relationship. Now please, just clear up will you? I do have a meal to prepare.

*(Exit **Rosie** to kitchen)*

Ben:
Platonic relationship?

Kelly: *(begins to tidy up)*
You know, like you and Melissa Curran, just good friends.

Ben: *(pensive)*
Huh. We have a love/hate relationship. I love her and she hates me.

*(**Kelly** picks up some papers and an open book left on the floor)*

Ben:
Hey, don't touch that!

Kelly:
Why, is it radioactive or something?

Ben: *(sarcastically)*
Funny. It's my history project. I left the book open at the right page, if you've lost the place –

Kelly: *(moves paper and books to coffee table)*
All right, I'll leave it over here. Didn't realize your history project meant so much to you.

Ben:
Can't seem to get interested in it, boring local history, but I've got to write the first part by Monday. Hey, Kell, what do you reckon my chances are of joining Greenspace?

Kelly: *(close up)*
Greenspace? With Lavinia and April? Are you feeling all right?

Ben:
Yeah, well, I'm interested in the environment, thought I could contribute.

Kelly:
You are ill.

· ·

6 Apartment   *int. evening*

*(**Giles, Ben, Kelly, Rosie** seated round dining table)*

Giles: *(finishing dessert)*
That was delicious, Rosie. You must give me the recipe. What do you call it?

Rosie:
Trifle Surprise.

Giles:
Oh, and what was the surprise?

Kelly:
Somebody likes it.

*(**Kelly** gets a playful cuff round the ear from **Rosie**)*

Giles:
No, no, it has a certain tang. It grows on you.

Ben: *(aside to **Kelly**)*
Yeah, so does Bubonic plague.

Rosie:
I'll make some coffee then.

(She exits to kitchen)

Giles: *(shouting through to **Rosie**)*
I don't know how you do it, Rosie. Can't be easy bringing up teenagers today and working full-time in the planning office.

*(**Kelly** and **Ben** look at each other)*

Giles: *(continuing)*
I was telling Dave in the office today you look far too young to have teenage children.

Kelly:
Vomit city!

Ben:
Yuk. Get the sick bag out.

Giles: *(to **Ben**)*
What?

Ben:
Oh, nothing.

Rosie: *(out of vision)*
How's the business going?

Giles:
Up and down. The problems I get, you wouldn't believe. . .

*(**Kelly** and **Ben** yawn)*

Giles: *(sipping wine)*
Do you know I had a client in last week, got a thousand Gazza T-shirts for sale, strictly unofficial ones, of course. He wanted my advice because he can't sell one of them.

Kelly:
Why, because they're unofficial? Like pirate tapes?

Giles:
Oh, no, that's not the problem. The berk's had them printed the wrong way up. Gazza's face is upside down on every one.

Ben:
So what did you advise him to do? Dump them all?

Giles:
Of course not. I used my initiative. Wrap them up in plastic bags and turn them the other way round, I told him, no one will ever notice the difference. You can sell them on market stalls or on the way to football grounds and by the time people discover the truth, it's too late. He paid me five hundred quid for solving that problem!

Ben:
But that's dishonest.

Giles:
All's fair in love and business, sunshine. Besides, I'm just the middleman, the entrepreneur who sets up the deals and gives advice. I didn't actually *sell* the T-shirts.

Kelly:
I think it stinks. As Proudhon said, 'All property is theft'.

Giles:
Did he? Probably explains why Proudhon never had a gleaming red Porsche in his garage like I do!

Ben:
And you think your car really impresses people?

Giles: *(looks knowingly towards **Rosie** in the kitchen)*
I know it does, I know it does.

*(**Rosie** enters and starts to clear plates away, **Giles** winks at **Kelly** and **Ben**)*

Rosie:
Glad to see you three are getting on so well. Picking up a few business tips for the future, Ben?

Ben:
Oh, yes, we're learning quite a bit here.

Giles:
Actually, Rosie, I'm working on a big deal at the moment.

Rosie: *(enthusiastic)*
Really?

Giles: *(taps his nose)*
Yeah, but I'm not really supposed to say anything at this stage. Strictly hush-hush.

Kelly:
Well that's the end of that conversation.

Giles: *(persisting)*
Yeah, this company's looking for a site to dump hundreds of tons of toxic waste but it's a bit sensitive at the moment, as you can imagine.

Rosie:
What sort of toxic waste?

Giles:
I don't know, old pesticides I think. Apparently, they used to dump everything in a nearby lake but the locals got wind of the operation. So now they're looking for another site, somewhere out of the way to avoid all the hassle.

Rosie:
And they've asked you to find somewhere?

Giles:
That's right. Course, we're keeping it quiet because we don't want all these 'do-gooders' interfering and spoiling the deal.

Kelly:
But surely that's illegal? You can't dump poisons anywhere.

Giles:
I'm not dumping poisons anywhere! I've told the company the stuff will be disposed of properly.

*(**Kelly** and **Ben** look at each other in disbelief)*

Giles:
It's all perfectly safe and above board. Look, I'm doing the community a favour, protecting the environment. If I can't find somewhere who knows what will happen to the stuff? Probably end up in our drinking water. I've thought all this out, you know.

Rosie:
I'm sure you have. I think Giles deserves some credit for his 'green enterprise'.

Giles:
Well thank you, Rosie. I like that. 'Green enterprise', yes, I think that pretty well sums up the operation. Of course, if I can find the right site, could be worth half a million in the first year alone.

*(**Giles** gets up, still drinking, and wanders over to coffee table. He looks at Ben's history project)*

Giles: *(picking up papers)*
What's this? 'A Day in the Life of a Manor house'?

As much as 86% of hazardous waste is disposed of in landfill sites — in other words, simply buried in the ground.

Ben: *(bored)*
It's my history project. For school. We have to do a local study.

Kelly: *(sarcastic)*
I'm sure Giles has no interest in that.

Giles:
Well that's just where you're wrong. See here, Ben. Fortescue Hall.

*(**Giles** prods page)*

Kelly:
Never heard of it.

Giles:
Of course you haven't. It was demolished years ago. But the Fortescues were aristocrats here for centuries. I wouldn't be at all surprised to discover I'm a descendant of theirs.

Ben:
What?

Giles:
Can't prove it, of course, but I wouldn't be surprised. We Fortescues came over with William the Conqueror, you know.

Rosie:
And you've been conquering the business world ever since!

*(**Ben** and **Kelly** groan)*

Giles: *(exaggerated laugh)*
Oh, very good, very good. So, er, Ben, where did you get all this information from?

Ben:
Local library – the historical collection.

Giles:
Perhaps I'll look them up sometime.

Kelly:
Fortescue, isn't that French for village idiot?

Giles:
What a shame you haven't inherited your mother's subtle sense of humour, Kelly.

Ben:
Well it's funnier than a Gazza T-shirt with the face upside down.

Rosie: *(still clearing dishes)*
What on earth is he talking about?

Giles: *(puts down **Ben's** papers)*
Nothing to worry about. Listen, you shouldn't be doing that, Rosie. Fancy a quick drink somewhere? I'm sure your lovely children won't mind washing up.

Ben:
What?

Giles: *(to **Rosie**)*
It's the very least I can do to thank you for your excellent hospitality.

Rosie:
Well, I don't know. . .

Kelly: *(getting up)*
Go on Mum, we'll do it.

Rosie:
All right then, just for an hour.

Giles: *(takes plates from **Rosie** and piles them on table again in front of **Ben**)*
Come madam, your carriage awaits.

*(**Rosie** grabs coats and walks off arm in arm with **Giles**, laughing. **Giles** smirks at **Ben** who stares dismally at the plates on the table)*

Kelly:
What a plonker!

Ben:
Yeah, and what a day!

7   *Playground*   *ext. day*

*(**Kyle** and **Ben** approach small group of kids, including **Lavinia** and **April**)*

Lavinia:
Oh look, April, it's Bill and Ben the carving knife men!

Kyle:
Ha, ha. Sarcasm is the lowest form of wit.

April: *(giggles)*
I thought it was a *cutting* remark!

Ben:
Listen, Lavinia, we've been thinking.

Lavinia:
Impossible!

Ben:
About your Greenspace Club. . . I'd like to join.

*(**Lavinia** and **April** stare in disbelief)*

April:
Well, you can't.

Ben:
Why not?

Lavinia:
Because only highly developed forms of life can join Greenspace.

April:
Girls, for example.

Kyle:
That's sexist, that is.

Ben:
Yeah, it's not fair having a club just for girls.

Lavinia:
Common sense. You'd just muck around and spoil it.

Kyle:
No he wouldn't. He's deadly serious, this boy. Give him a chance.

Lavinia: *(taking **April** aside with a knowing wink)*
Well, we have to discuss this in private.

April: *(huddled conversation)*
We can't let idiots like him in.

Lavinia:
There's nothing in the rules to say we can't let boys in.

April:
Lavinia, you're not serious!

Lavinia:
Listen, first he'll have to appear before the Committee, then make a speech. Can you imagine what a fool he'll make of himself?

April: *(ponders)*
I suppose it could be rather amusing.

Lavinia:
Exactly. And remember, you and I have the right to veto any new application. He doesn't stand a chance.

*(**Lavinia** and **April** return to **Ben** and **Kyle**)*

Lavinia:
After careful consideration, we've decided that you can attend today's meeting after school.

Ben:
Oh, great. Does that mean I'm in, then?

April:
Let's not jump to conclusions. We are very choosy about our members.

Lavinia:
I must warn you that we have the power of veto.

*(**Lavinia** and **April** walk off sniggering)*

Ben:
Veto? What does that mean?

Kyle:
It means, my son, that I'll probably get to keep my Iron Maiden album!

Ben: *(shaking head)*
No, no. I'm on my way, Kyle. Don't you see it's a sign? My luck is changing! Melissa Curran, here I come.

. . . .

8 Dining room / common room   *int. day*

*(**Kyle** seated at table with **Ben** and **Jack**)*

Kyle: *(pushes **Ben**)*
Go on, tell her and be cool!

*(**Ben** walks over to nearby table where **Melissa** is sitting with **Carol** and another friend, eating chips. **Ben** reaches down and picks up tomato ketchup 'squeezy' holder)*

Ben:
Eh, excuse me, can I borrow this?

*(**Melissa** looks at friends and says nothing. Close up of **Melissa**'s bandaged finger)*

Ben:
Look, I just wanted to say sorry – about your finger I mean – really stupid of me.

Carol:
You can say that again.

Ben:
Yeah well, um, hey. Guess what?

(No response from girls)

Ben: *(trying to sound cool)*
I'm joining Greenspace today. . . Reckon I've got to do my bit for the environment. . .

*(Camera close up – **Ben** is absent-mindedly squeezing tomato ketchup down his trousers without realizing it)*

Ben: *(smugly)*
Yeah, I thought to myself, Ben, it's about time you did something. Right Melissa? Make up for the accident yesterday.

Carol: *(noticing **Ben**'s trousers)*
Ben, I think you've had another accident.

*(**Carol** nods downwards. **Ben**'s smile fades. Close up of **Ben**'s trousers)*

Ben:
Oh, no!

*(Girls laugh. **Ben** tries to clean himself up, looking embarrassed. **Kyle** comes over, puts a consoling arm on **Ben's** shoulder)*

Kyle:
Don't know about Greenspace, mate, you look more like the Scarlet Pimpernel!

(More laughter)

9 *Greenspace committee room* *int. day*

*(**Lavinia** and **April** sit at table with pens / notepad, other members seated in circle, including **Ben** and **Kyle**. Scene begins with close up of **Grace** in middle of speech, addressing members from the floor)*

Grace:
Disgusting, degrading and a health hazard. The results of last week's survey show that in Room 42 alone we found one hundred and sixty-two assorted pieces of chewing gum stuck underneath the desks.

Kyle: *(aside to **Ben**)*
Sticky problem!

Other girls:
Shh!

Grace:
Furthermore, I move that the Committee recommends that all members of Greenspace will, in future, desist from chewing bubble gum, horror balls, jawcrushers. . .

Lavinia: *(interrupting)*
Yes, thank you, Grace, all in favour of the recommendation say 'Aye'.

All: *(except **Ben** who sheepishly empties his mouth of gum)*
Aye.

Grace:
And Madam Chairperson, may I also ask for a Greenspace volunteer to clean up the desks in Room 42 as soon as possible?

Lavinia:
Right, we'll appoint a volunteer later. Now, members, we come to the last item on the agenda, application for membership of Greenspace from Benjamin Turner.

Kyle: *(nudging **Ben**)*
Oh, Benjamin!

Ben:
Shut up.

Lavinia: *(approaching **Ben**)*
Will you please stand up and state your reason for wishing to join
Greenspace?

*(**Ben** rises awkwardly to his feet. All members fall silent. **Ben** looks
uncomfortable and glances briefly at **Melissa** on other side of room.
Kyle takes out pad to make notes)*

Ben: *(nervous and hesitant)*
Well, I think as a boy I can offer. . . um. . . something to the group
and. . . um. . . I agree with eh. . . the aims and of. . . um Greengage,
eh, Greenspace, and the chewing gum, I mean that is disgusting, I
agree something should be done. . .

*(**Kyle** looks up laughing, shaking his head)*

Ben:
And, eh. . . that's it really.

Lavinia:
That's it!

Ben:
Well. . . yeah.

April: *(rising to her feet)*
Members, that was the most pathetic speech we've ever listened to. I
know the real reason why he wants to join Greenspace. . .

*(**April** approaches **Ben** with an intimidating look)*

Because, members, he fancies Melissa.

(Other girls voice disapproval, shouts of 'shame')

Lavinia: *(raises hand for silence)*
Is this true?

*(**Ben** looks at **Melissa**, swallows hard. **Melissa** looks embarrassed)*

Ben:
I. . . eh. . . I. . .

Lavinia:
I don't think we need waste any more time. He obviously has nothing to contribute to our environmental campaign unit. Application rejected, I move. All in favour say 'Aye'.

(All members say 'Aye'. **Ben** *looks round in desperation)*

Ben:
No, wait. Shut up! Shut up! I can offer something. Toxic waste!

Lavinia:
What?

Ben:
Toxic waste. It's a. . . poisons from waste stuff and that. . .

Lavinia:
Yes, I am perfectly well aware of the definition of toxic waste but what has this got to do with you?

Ben:
Well, Greenspace is interested in environ. . . enviro. . . in protecting us all. . .

Lavinia:
Yes, yes, just get on with it.

Ben:
Yeah. . . well. . . you see, I've heard about this guy who's going to dump some toxic waste locally. . . it's all secret at the moment.

Lavinia:
What sort of toxic waste?

Ben:
I don't know. . . pesticides, I think.

Lavinia:
And where's this stuff being dumped?

Ben:
There's this company and they're looking for a secret site at this very moment. Don't you see, that's the whole point? They don't want people to find out.

April:
Are we going to listen to any more of this nonsense? He's obviously lying through his teeth!

Lavinia:
No, wait a moment, members. Ben, where did you get this information from?

Ben: *(tapping nose imitating **Giles**)*
Let's just say I have my contacts.

April: *(to members)*
This is absurd! His application has been rejected, he has no right to speak in this meeting.

Other members:
Here, here! Sit down!

Lavinia: *(angry)*
Silence! I will decide who speaks in our meetings as the duly elected Chairperson, thank you!

(Group quietens down)

Lavinia:
I might remind members this is not the House of Commons! Now then, we have a duty to pursue this story. If it is true we must act now to protect our community. Benjamin, will you be able to get any more information from your contact?

Ben:
Probably. . . yes. . . I will.

Lavinia:
Good. The dumping of pesticides, as you realize, members, poses a grave threat to our environment. Therefore, I propose that Benjamin

Turner be granted temporary membership of Greenspace until we can substantiate his story.

Ben: (*glancing towards* **Melissa** *and beaming*)
Brilliant!

Lavinia:
But we shall require further proof as soon as possible.

Ben:
Of course.

Lavinia:
And in the meantime we shall expect you to make a full contribution to our group.

Ben: (*smiling*)
A full contribution, right on man, sorry, Chairperson!

(**Lavinia** *gathers up papers and sweeps out of room.* **Kyle** *smacks* **Ben**'s *hand in recognition of his success*)

· ·

10 Classroom   *int. day*

(**Ben** *scraping chewing gum from underneath desks. Empty room except for* **Kyle** *who lounges against a desk watching* **Ben** *at work*)

Ben: (*turns desk on its side*)
Phew! The last one!

Kyle:
A little to the left, and scrapers ready, begin.

Ben: (*looking up disgruntled*)
Thanks for your help, pal.

Kyle:
I'm management, besides, this is *your* contribution, remember?

Ben: *(starts scraping again)*
Yes, all right. And how many of these bits are yours?

Kyle: *(picking up piece of hardened gum from floor)*
Hard to say. Wait a minute. Ah, an amusing little number – now let me see. . .

(Sniffs piece)

. . . I would say this is vintage, yes, definitely double geography Friday afternoon March 1991.

Ben:
Just put it in the bin.

Kyle: *(throws piece of gum in bin and salutes)*
Yes sir, Mr Greenspace officer.

Ben: *(standing up)*
Not yet. Not yet. But you should have seen Melissa's face when I told them about that toxic waste.

Kyle:
OK, so that was a nice move. But – but how are you going to prove it? Lavinia wants an answer tomorrow.

*(Enter **Lavinia**)*

Lavinia:
Yes, Lavinia wants an answer tomorrow.

Kyle: *(looking at **Ben**, pretending not to notice **Lavinia**)*
Is there a parrot in here?

Lavinia:
No parrots, more like a couple of donkeys, I would say.

Kyle:
Oh, hee-haw. You're so funny Lavinia. Anyway, old Ben's doing a good job here.

*(**Lavinia** moves over to desk where **Ben** is working)*

Lavinia:
So I see, no thanks to you, Kyle.

Kyle:
Hey, don't underestimate the great Kyle. I'm a vital cog in the machine, I'm keeping his morale going.

Lavinia:
Highly unlikely, now would you mind leaving? I want to talk to Ben. Alone.

Kyle:
Oooo!!

Lavinia:
Committee business and I don't recall your name on our list of members.

Kyle:
All right. All right. I'll leave you two lovebirds on your own.

*(**Kyle** moves towards door and blows kisses in the direction of **Lavinia**)*

Ben:
Shut up!

Lavinia: *(calling)*
Oh, Kyle!

*(**Kyle** stops in doorway and looks back)*

Lavinia:
Actually, the correct terminology is 'keeping morale up', not 'going'.

*(**Kyle** smirks and slams door)*

Lavinia:
He's pathetic.

*(**Ben** is still scraping desk)*

Ben:
You don't like Kyle, do you?

Lavinia:
You've noticed? Look, he has no right to interfere in Greenspace business. In future keep him away please.

Ben:
He's my best mate. He told me to join Greenspace in the first place.

Lavinia:
Really? I thought Melissa Curran had something to do with that.

*(**Ben** looks uncomfortable)*

Ben:
I've finished all the desks.

Lavinia:
Good. Now, we need more information about this dumping of toxic waste.

Ben:
I told you yesterday at the meeting. . . that's all I know, Lavinia, honest. . .

Lavinia:
That's not enough. We must have more details if we are to fight an active campaign. We need to know exactly what's going on.

Ben: *(sighing)*
Giles is coming round again tonight. I could ask him again, but. . . you don't understand, Lavinia, he doesn't like me very much.

Lavinia:
No, *you* don't understand. I spoke up for you in Committee yesterday. Now I expect results.

*(**Lavinia** moves towards door then turns)*

Lavinia:
If you let me down, it's goodbye Greenspace and it's goodbye Melissa. I'll make certain of that.

*(**Lavinia** smiles sweetly then slams door. **Ben**, left on his own, pushes desk to one side looking glum)*

· ·

11   Apartment   *int. day*

*(**Kelly** and **Ben** sit at dining room table. **Kelly** is applying small plasters to **Ben**'s fingers)*

Kelly:
Hold still, will you?

Ben:
It hurts.

Kelly:
Don't be such a baby, if Melissa could see you now.

Ben:
My fingers are all blistered, put some cream on that one.

Kelly:
It's your own fault for scraping all those desks.

Ben: *(winces in pain)*
I did it for Greenspace.

Kelly:
Oh yeah? If you ask me you're green and the only space is between your ears.

*(**Ben** shakes his hands/fingers. Enter **Giles** from the kitchen area, swaggers over to table carrying bottle of sparkling wine)*

Giles: *(jovial mood)*
Well, hello Benjamin.

*(**Giles** looks at **Kelly**)*

Giles:
Have you told him the good news yet?

Ben:
What, you leaving already?

Giles: *(leaning over **Ben**, puts bottle on table)*
Listen peasant, you are now addressing a member of the aristocracy.

Ben: *(to **Kelly**)*
What's he on about? Have you been drinking, Giles?

Giles: *(pulls out large envelope)*
Certainly have, this is the reason we're celebrating.

*(**Giles** pulls out photocopies of letters and old manuscript, and throws them on table)*

Giles: *(pointing to top of one document)*
You see that name at the top? The Fortescues, owners of the largest estate in the county years ago. Remember, I said I wouldn't be surprised if I was related to them.

Ben: *(disbelief)*
You're not.

Giles: *(sits down opposite **Ben**. **Kelly** moves off)*
I am a direct descendant of Sir Henry Fortescue, Lord of the Manor in 1450.

Ben:
Who says?

Giles:
Ah! The records say. My solicitor's checked them out. My ancestors were the Fortescues of Fortescue Hall. See? I knew I was different from the crowd, singled out to be the chosen one. Fancy that, me related to the Lord of the Manor!

*(Enter **Rosie**)*

Rosie:
Heard Giles' news?

Ben:
I can hardly contain my excitement. Anyway, that was in 1450. He's not Lord of the Manor now.

Rosie: *(excited – joins **Giles**)*
But that's not all.

*(**Giles** unfolds large map on table)*

Giles:
No, that's not all. This is the rest. . . Blackberry Way.

(Thumps map to emphasize)

Ben:
Blackberry Way?

Rosie:
You know, that piece of waste land at the end of the by-pass.

Ben:
Yeah, I know, me and Kelly used to go blackberrying there.

Giles:
When we checked the land records we discovered that Blackberry Way actually belonged to the Fortescues, it was part of their estate. Apparently, they were forced to sell two fields to the Government in 1795 when we were at war with France, something about needing to grow more food. When the war was over the Government should have sold Blackberry Way back to the Fortescues for the same price. But they never did. So my ancestors were done out of five acres.

Ben: *(shrugs)*
But I still don't get it.

Giles:
Well, the deeds state that Blackberry Way should be sold back to the Fortescues and as I'm the only living descendant that means me!

Rosie:
Tell him the price, Giles.

Giles:
This is the good bit. They have to sell it back to me now for the original price they paid for it in 1795 which was one hundred pounds. So I'm getting five acres of land for just a hundred quid!

Ben:
So, you're getting a piece of land for a hundred pounds, what can you do with it? Build a manor house?

Giles:
You seem to have forgotten my new role as the local consultant for environmental issues.

Ben:
The pesticide dump?

Giles:
Exactly. It's the ideal site I've been looking for, out of the way, won't affect anybody.

Kelly:
But kids play on there. It could be dangerous.

Giles:
When it's my land there won't be any kids playing there. Private property, it will be strictly out of bounds. I'm not having anybody snooping around. Besides, there's no danger involved.

Ben:
How do you know this stuff isn't dangerous?

Giles:
No problem. I'll just mix the stuff with household rubbish and bury it in the ground. Concrete the whole thing over and then I'll probably sell the land for office development, nobody will be any the wiser.

Kelly:
And you'll make a fat profit out of it, no doubt.

Giles:
A cool half million I'd say. Business is business!

Ben:
But you can't do that.

Giles: *(rising from table)*
Oh yes I can. It's my land now and nobody can do anything about it.
Here's the proof. Read it for yourself.

*(Throws document at **Ben**)*

Giles:
And you know what, old boy?

Ben:
What?

Giles:
It's all down to you.

*(**Ben** looks up, puzzled)*

Rosie:
You see after Giles looked at your history project, he decided to do
some research himself. He followed up the Fortescue records in the
local library and discovered the bit about Blackberry Way.

Kelly: *(sarcastically)*
You're so clever, Giles.

*(**Giles** moves over to **Rosie** and puts arm around her)*

Giles:
That's history. And when I'm finished with Blackberry Way I shall
be Lord of the Manor again and you shall be my lady.

*(**Kelly** pulls a face and groans)*

Giles:
Yes, I think I'll take a ride out to Blackberry Way on Saturday and
survey my new estate.

*(**Giles** picks up glass and walks back to table, putting glass in front of **Ben**)*

Giles:
Here you are, Ben, have some wine to celebrate my best deal ever.

*(**Giles** tips up bottle and two tiny drops left in bottle fall into the glass)*

Giles:
Not much left I'm afraid, old boy. Never mind, I've saved you a stick of chewing gum instead.

*(**Giles** throws down piece of gum on table laughing)*

. . . .

12   *Playground*   *ext. day*

*(**Ben** in huddled conversation with **Lavinia** and **April**, shows them document and letter)*

Ben:
There's your proof.

Lavinia:
Blackberry Way. It's obscene.

April:
It's gross. We used to have picnics there.

Ben:
But it's true. Blackberry Way will disappear under a mountain of concrete and pesticide.

April:
But surely what he's doing is illegal?

Ben:
Of course it is, but he'll deny everything. The dumping will be done in secret so no one will know.

Lavinia:
Until the mercury from the pesticide leaks into the soil and by then it will be far too late.

Ben:
And Giles Fortescue will be worth a million.

April:
We must find a way to stop this. Under the Environmental Act –

Lavinia: *(interrupting)*
April, get everyone in the group together. We'll call a special meeting at lunchtime in the Committee Room. This is time for action! Well, go on!

*(**April** moves off quickly, **Lavinia** continues to scan letter)*

Lavinia:
So Fortescue is going to Blackberry Way tomorrow?

Ben:
That's what he said. He wants to see his new estate before he signs the papers.

Lavinia:
Perfect. We'll organize a protest march.

Ben:
Huh, that won't stop him.

Lavinia:
Probably not, so we must be prepared to use guerrilla tactics.

Ben: *(imitates monkey sounds)*
Ooo. . . Oooo. . .

*(**Lavinia** looks up in disgust)*

Ben:
Sorry, sorry. Guerrilla tactics, I like the sound of that. So what are we going to do?

Lavinia:
I'm still thinking.

Ben:
I know. We could pelt him with flour bombs. Yes!

Lavinia:
Benjamin, please! Greenspace is more sophisticated than that.

Ben:
Go on, let me. I'd love to smack him in the gob with a flour bomb.

Lavinia:
Certainly not. We must use subtle means to achieve our objectives.
Look, according to this letter Fortescue has to sign the contract for
the land with the Council by noon tomorrow.

Ben:
I know. Giles wants the deal to go through as quickly as possible.

Lavinia:
Yes, I bet he does! Any delay could ruin the deal for him if people
became suspicious and started asking awkward questions.

(Pauses for thought)

Lavinia:
Blackberry Way must be at least five miles from the Council offices.

Ben:
So?

Lavinia:
So, if we can prevent Fortescue from getting back to the Town Hall
by twelve o'clock tomorrow, then he won't be able to sign the
contract, will he?

Ben:
How do we do that?

Lavinia:
Leave that to me. Here, take your letter back before Fortescue notices it's missing.

*(**Ben** takes back letter)*

Ben:
Don't worry about that. He was so busy celebrating last night he left all his papers on the table.

Lavinia:
Well, he won't look so happy tomorrow. I'll meet you in the Committee Room later.

· ·

13   *Greenspace committee room*   *int. day*

*No dialogue. All members of Greenspace are active. **Lavinia** points out route on large map on wall, other members kneel on floor making banners and posters. Scissors, paper, glue, wood, everywhere. Occasional close up shots of different activities, e.g. lettering on posters, cutting out cards, writing, **Lavinia** in the centre organizing everyone. **Ben** darts about helping here and there. Music sound-track accompaniment.*

· ·

14 *Playground*   *ext. day*

*(Greenspace marchers assemble carrying banners, posters, chatting excitedly. **Lavinia** and **April** close up in centre)*

Lavinia:
I told Ben to be here at ten o'clock.

April:
I knew we couldn't rely on him.

Lavinia: *(looks at watch)*
Can't wait any longer. We shall have to start without him.

During the Gulf War in 1991 a vast oil-slick devastated the Persian Gulf, killing birds and marine life. Environmentalists are still counting the cost. The region will probably never recover.

(*Lavinia* assembles marchers, places herself at the front of group)

Lavinia:
Ready everybody? Let's go!

(*Marchers in good humour leave playground area*)

All: (*chanting*)
Save Blackberry Way!

(*Repeat to fade*)

. . . .

15 Blackberry Way   *ext. day*

(*Rural area, with trees, bushes, grass.*) (**Giles** *wearing green wellies slowly surveys the site at Blackberry Way, strutting with map in hand. Suddenly a plastic ball flies through the air and hits him on the head. He folds map away, looking annoyed, and picks up ball. Two young children run up to* **Giles**)

First child:
Sorry mate, can we have our ball back?

Giles: (*slowly*)
Yes, you can have your ball back.

(**Giles** *squashes ball out of shape*)

Giles:
Here it is.

(**Giles** *hands ball to second child, smirking*)

Second child:
You've squashed it!

Giles:
Have I? Tough. Now get off my land before *you* get squashed.

(First child kicks Giles on shin and runs away. In the distance, sound of chanting becomes louder. Giles looks round and watches Greenspace protestors moving towards him)

Giles:
What the heck is this?

(Protestors march right up to Giles. Lavinia, April, Grace at the front. Lavinia silences marchers)

Giles:
And what is the meaning of this?

Lavinia: *(forceful)*
We are Greenspace and we are protesting against the redevelopment of Blackberry Way.

April: *(nodding in agreement)*
We do not want poison dumped here.

Giles: *(taken aback)*
And what do you mean by that?

Grace:
We're fighting for the common person, for the rights of the individual to live according to his or her needs in a world that isn't swallowed up in concrete and steel, where people are put first before profit, where our green and precious land is retained for future generations. . .

Giles: *(holds hands up in protest)*
All right, all right, I've heard enough of this claptrap. Now for your information, you are trespassing on my land so you can take your greenies and go.

Lavinia:
So you're Giles Fortescue? Well, we have a petition here signed by all our members.

(Lavinia holds up petition to cheers from group)

Giles: *(irritated)*
Look, I couldn't care less if the Queen had signed your stupid petition. This is my land now and I can do what I like with it. It's none of your business so clear off before I call the police.

Lavinia:
It's not your land yet.

Giles:
Well it will be in a few minutes.

*(**Giles** gloats)*

Lavinia:
I doubt it. We reckon it's about five miles from here to the Town Hall. That's a very long way to walk.

Giles:
What are you talking about?

Lavinia:
That red sports car parked at the end of the field belongs to you, I believe.

Giles: *(expression changing)*
If you've damaged my car. . .

April:
All we've done is tie some green balloons on it.

Greenspace girl:
And painted some slogans on the side.

Giles:
What!!!

April:
And I forgot to mention the wheel clamps.

Giles:
You. . . you hooligans! How dare you! I shall call the police immediately.

Lavinia:
Calm down, calm down, Mr Fortescue. April's only joking. We haven't touched your car.

Giles:
Lucky for you.

Lavinia:
But you shouldn't have parked your car in the field. We had to close the gate behind you.

April:
And padlock it.

Lavinia:
Part of the Countryside Code, you see. My members are very conscientious. We must close all gates to prevent animals from escaping into the road.

Giles:
There are no animals here.

Lavinia:
Really? Oh dear, our mistake. April, you better go and unlock the gate so that Mr Fortescue can get his car out. I believe he has an important meeting in town.

April:
Well, I would, Lavinia, but I can't seem to find the key.

(*April* searches through pockets)

April:
I must have dropped it somewhere.

(Rest of group laugh and cheer)

Lavinia:
And it's such a large area. What a pity, Mr Fortescue, it will take simply ages to find the key. Never mind, I'm sure it will turn up by nightfall!

Giles: *(laughing)*
Do you really think you can stop me signing for this land by twelve o'clock?

Lavinia:
Unless you plan to be air-lifted out of here by helicopter, I should say that's a foregone conclusion.

*(**Lavinia** checks watch, others cheer again)*

Giles:
Wrong. You lot are so stupid. The Town Hall doesn't open on Saturdays. Mr Taylor from the Council is bringing me the papers here to sign. In fact, he should be on his way now. What do you think of that, Miss Rent-a-mouth?

Lavinia:
I think you are an arrogant, egotistical, three-dimensional cabbage stalk.

*(Others cheer **Lavinia**)*

Giles:
Words, just words. Let's face it, you've lost.

*(**Giles** looks over the heads of the protestors)*

Giles:
In fact, I can see Taylor coming now.

*(Protestors subdued as **Mr Taylor** pushes his way through crowd, followed by **Rosie** and **Ben**. **Giles** notices **Rosie**)*

Giles:
What are you doing here?

Rosie:
Listen, Giles, there's something you ought to know –

Mr Taylor: *(pushing in front of **Rosie**)*
Sorry we're late, Mr Fortescue. Some idiot locked the gate and we had to stagger across this scrubland.

Giles:
Never mind that. Have you got all the papers?

Mr Taylor:
They're all here.

Giles:
Good. I want to sign them right now, in front of this rabble.

Rosie:
No, wait, Giles, we need to discuss this.

Giles:
There's nothing else to discuss.

*(**Giles** snatches papers from **Taylor**, gets out pen)*

Giles:
Right, now I sign here at the bottom.

Rosie:
Giles, will you please listen to me for a moment. . .

Mr Taylor: *(pointing out correct place for **Giles**)*
That's it, Mr Fortescue, right there on the dotted line.

Giles: *(signs papers and hands them back to **Taylor**)*
There. The all-important signature. Am I or am I not the new owner of Blackberry Way?

Mr Taylor:
Oh, indeed you are, sir, indeed you are. Congratulations.

Giles:
Beautiful. Beautiful. Victory is sweet, eh, ladies?

*(**Giles** smirks at **Lavinia** and friends. Crowd boo. **Ben** puts his hands up to appeal for silence)*

Lavinia: *(to **Ben**)*
And thanks for all your help this morning. I might have known you'd let us down when it came to the crunch.

The main components of acid rain are sulphur dioxide and nitrogen oxides. In 1988, power stations were responsible for 71% of sulphur dioxide emissions. The UK produces more sulphur dioxide than any other EC country.

Giles:
Ignore them, Ben, it's just sour grapes. They can't take defeat.

Ben:
Listen. I went to the Record Office this morning with Mum to check all the details. Just in case there was a mistake. But there isn't. Giles Fortescue does own this land and there's nothing we can do about it.

Giles:
You're learning, Ben.

Ben:
Yep. You're the new owner of Blackberry Way.

Giles: *(smugly)*
Right.

Ben:
And the blackberries.

Giles:
What?

Ben: *(pulling document from pocket)*
You see, Giles, you didn't read the small print.

*(**Ben** unfolds document)*

Ben:
Sir Henry Fortescue, your ancestor, granted an ancient right to the children of the village that they should always be allowed to play in this area and pick blackberries when in season.

Giles: *(snatches document)*
Let me see that.

*(**Giles** studies letter)*

Giles:
This can't be true.

Ben:
Yes it is. You can't touch a thing on this land. You've got to preserve this area for us and keep the blackberry bushes in good order. Ancient rights. Amazing, I never thought a history project could be so interesting, eh Giles?

Giles: *(to **Rosie**)*
Why didn't you stop me signing?

Rosie:
I tried but you wouldn't listen!

Giles: *(to **Mr Taylor**)*
You deceived me. . . you deceived me. . . I'll sue, I'll sue the Council for every penny you've got!

Mr Taylor:
Oh, I don't think you will, Mr Fortescue. After all, I mean it would be terrible if the land were used for something else. . . like the dumping of poisons, for example. That would be a great blow to your image as the new Lord of the Manor, wouldn't it, Mr Fortescue?

Ben:
Looks like you've been done, Giles. Never mind, old boy, business is business!

*(**Giles** storms away)*

Ben: *(shouting)*
Oh, Giles.

Giles: *(turning)*
What?

Ben:
I didn't have any chewing gum. Here, have this instead.

*(**Ben** throws tin to **Giles** who catches it. Close up camera shows tin of blackberries. **Giles** walks off scowling, Greenspace members surround **Ben** cheering and congratulating him)*

16 Greenspace committee room   int. day

*(Close up: **Ben** is standing in centre of room on box. Other members surround him. **Lavinia** approaches)*

Lavinia: *(very solemn)*
And so, for his achievement in saving Blackberry Way, we award our new member, Benjamin Turner, the Greenspace Medal of Honour.

*(**Lavinia** places medal on chain or ribbon around **Ben**'s neck. Burst of applause from all members, who clap and cheer. Camera close up of **Ben** who looks around, searching out **Melissa** who is nowhere to be seen)*

. . . .

17 Corridor   int. day

*(**Ben** hurries down corridor wearing medal, looking excited and pleased with himself. He stops abruptly. **Ben**'s smile disappears. Camera from behind **Ben** shows **Kyle** and **Melissa** directly ahead. **Kyle** has his arm round **Melissa** in affectionate embrace. Camera close up. **Kyle** glances sideways and suddenly notices **Ben** watching. Pull back camera. **Kyle** quickly releases **Melissa** and turns towards **Ben**)*

Kyle: *(hesitant and embarrassed)*
Oh, hi Ben, I was just. . . eh. . .

*(Close up **Ben**. He looks hurt and then angry. He tears medal from his neck and throws it at **Kyle**'s feet. He looks at **Kyle** and then **Melissa**. In disgust **Ben** turns away and storms off. **Kyle** holds his hands up in a gesture of innocence as he watches **Ben** go)*

. . . .

18 Dining room / common room   int. day

*(One month later. Camera close up – **Kyle** and **Melissa** sitting at table, laughing and talking. Pull back shot from above, **Ben** surveys the scene. Turns and faces camera – close up shot)*

Ben: *(wearing medal again)*
Am I bitter? Am I jealous? You bet I am! Still, I've learnt something. All that glitters is not gold. There are more important things in life, like saving Blackberry Way. Oh yeah, I'm a fully paid up member of Greenspace now and I've got my medal back. And you know what? It's all down to one girl, Lavinia Holdsworth. She's changed me for the better.

Lavinia: *(out of vision)*
There you are. Where have you been?

Ben: *(glances sideways)*
But then, I've changed her as well.

*(Pulls back camera revealing **Lavinia** who is dressed in leather jacket, torn jeans. She wears her hair long and loose. She is no longer wearing glasses. **Ben** winks at the camera and goes off arm in arm with **Lavinia**)*

Activities

What the Author Says

Is **The Teen Commandments** a play dealing with relationships between boys and girls? Or is it simply a green comedy? The answer to both questions is probably 'yes'. I hope that you will be able to identify with the characters and situations in the play by drawing on your own experiences. I also recognize how important environmental issues have become in our world today.

Most of the action centres around the Greenspace environmental group, but the comedy develops from the characters and their actions, not from the group itself. It is people who make comedy, not issues.

I also set out to explore in the play how we use other people, and situations, to gain friendships, rewards, and even revenge. Ben uses Greenspace because he fancies Melissa. Lavinia uses Greenspace to show everyone how important she is. In the end, both characters unite to prevent Giles from ruining Blackberry Way and yet both have different reasons for wanting to achieve this. Kyle uses Greenspace to poke fun at Lavinia and at the same time deceives his best friend.

In the opening scenes you probably think that Ben is a wimp, but he emerges as the hero in the end. He saves Blackberry Way and manages to stop the greedy Giles in the process. Ben may lose the girl of his dreams on the way but he gains the friendship and trust of Lavinia, not an easy thing to do.

The play has been written for video production in schools but can easily be adapted for classroom reading and stage work. You may like to explore some of the more important issues raised in a variety of ways. Hopefully, the Activities Section will give you that opportunity.

My own drama group, who contributed some of the ideas in the Activities section, have taught me one thing above all else – acting should be fun. I hope that you will enjoy performing **The Teen Commandments**.

Kelvin Reynolds

The Top 'Teen Commandments'

1 Hi-fi units shall always have two volume controls – loud and very loud.

2 Anyone over the age of twenty shall be referred to as an 'oldie' or 'fogey'.

3 You shall never telephone a friend until *Neighbours* is finished.

4 When asked to do a household chore by parents you shall always reply 'I'll do it in a minute.'

5 February 29th shall be set aside for tidying your room.

6 You shall always say that your best friend gets more pocket money than you.

7 ....

8 ....

9 ....

10 ....

Discuss   **In pairs**

How many of the above 'Commandments' apply to you? Add four more commandments of your own to complete the ten. Make a list of all the jobs you do at home.

Read   'The trouble with teenagers today is that they're totally selfish. They only think about themselves. They have too much money, too much freedom and if you say anything to them all you get is a load of abuse.'

Write   Do you think that this is a fair assessment of teenage behaviour today? Why/why not?

Body Language

The Teen Commandments is a visual play with the emphasis on what is *seen*. Television and video scripts rely enormously on characters conveying their thoughts and feelings through expression and movement. This form of communication is known as *Body Language*.

Discuss

In pairs

Study the following photographs taken from scenes in the play, and answer the questions that follow.

Photograph A Scene 2. A troubled Ben tells Kyle and Jack about Melissa.
How can you tell from this picture that Ben is very worried?
Do you think Kyle and Jack share his concern?

Photograph B Scene 3. Kyle says, 'Let's have some fun,' when he sees Lavinia working on her project.
What do you think Kyle is planning to do?
Why does Kyle pick on Lavinia?

Photograph C Scene 7. Ben asks to join Greenspace but Lavinia and April are not impressed.
How can you tell this from the girls' reactions?

Photograph D Scene 9. Greenspace committee room.
How can you tell from this picture that Lavinia (seated left) is the leader of the group?

Photograph E Scene 9. Ben makes his speech at the meeting.
How do you know that Kyle is not taking a serious interest in the meeting?

Photograph F Scene 17. Ben discovers Kyle and Melissa.
How do you think Kyle feels at this moment?
What is Melissa's reaction?

Photographs G and H Compare the two photographs of Lavinia. In photograph G, Lavinia (centre) prepares the Greenspace protest. Photograph H shows Lavinia at the end of the play. How has she changed?

Drama Ideas

Improvise

Reactions

Try out the following ideas, individually or in pairs, using body language. Concentrate on facial expressions and also the way you are sitting or standing. Remember not to use any words!

1 **Surprise or excitement**. Your best friend has just given you a ticket for a pop concert at the weekend.

2 **Dejection**. Your mother has just forbidden you to attend the concert.

3 **Boredom**. The most boring person in the class is sitting next to you relating in great detail their recent holiday abroad.

4 **Anxiety**. A note has arrived in your register summoning you immediately to the Headteacher's office.

5 **Fear**. Two older pupils with a reputation for bullying follow you across a deserted park and eventually corner you.
OR There's a spider in the bath!

6 **Concern**. Your best friend is planning to run away from home.

7 **Embarrassment**. In front of the whole school, you are asked to stand up in Assembly for talking.

8 **Curiosity**. A large parcel is waiting for you on the kitchen table.

You may also wish to develop your own ideas and get someone in the class to take photographs of each scene to capture your expression and movement. This is an ideal preparation for video filming.

Boy/Girl Relationships

Ben tries hard to impress Melissa throughout the play. He is shocked to find her with Kyle.

Improvise   **1**   Act out the following situations in pairs.

- Kyle tries to explain to Ben why he wants to go out with Melissa.
- Lavinia asks Melissa to resign from Greenspace.
- Ben confronts Melissa and demands to know what is going on.
- Melissa tries to justify her actions.
- April wants to be the new leader of Greenspace because she thinks Lavinia has changed.

       2   Ben uses Greenspace as an excuse to get to know Melissa better. In an imaginary telephone conversation to a friend, describe your feelings about a new girl or boy in your class, whom you like very much. Ask your friend for any ideas or suggestions on how to get to know this person better.

Write   **1**   April doesn't want Ben to join Greenspace because, in her opinion, 'Boys would only muck about and spoil it.' Do you agree with this statement? Write a short piece either supporting this view or explaining the reasons why you disagree with April.

2   Melissa (seen in the photograph below) does not have any lines to say in the play. Why do you think the author decided that Melissa should be 'seen and not heard'?

Write a paragraph explaining your feelings about Melissa's role in the play.

Protests

Think

Lavinia decides to organize a Greenspace protest march against the Council's plan to sell the Blackberry Way site to Giles. Apart from the march, think of other ways of protesting against the plan that Lavinia might have considered instead.

Improvise **1**

In groups of eight to twelve people, organize a protest march as part of a drama lesson. Choose an issue that you feel strongly about. Some of the group could design appropriate banners on placards, others could suggest a suitable chant to be used on the march.

2

In small groups, act out the following situation.
A group of local residents from a small village have organized a 'sit down' protest in the road against the number of heavy lorries using the village as a short cut. The residents are very worried at the increasing risk of accidents and are also concerned about the noise and pollution.

Suggestions for characters might include a worried parent, an angry lorry driver, a policeman called to the scene, a newspaper reporter covering the story. An extension of this scene may also involve one or two people being interviewed by radio or television news reporters.

Write

Imagine that you are one of the residents from the village. Write a letter to your local Member of Parliament explaining why you feel so strongly about this issue.

Discuss

Study carefully the photograph opposite, taken at the scene of the London Poll Tax riot in March, 1990.

What is happening in this picture?

Why is it that some protest marches can start peacefully but end in violence?

Do you think that the use of violence can ever be justified in any form of protest?

Do you think that Lavinia in the future might ever be tempted to use violence like the girl shown in the photograph?

The Environment

1 The environmental poster below was designed by Elizabeth Wallace, a pupil at Sawston Village College. Study it carefully. Try and explain what is happening in your own words.

2 Design your own environmental poster. You may wish to concentrate on local issues affecting your school or town, such as noise, litter, and the dumping of rubbish, or you might consider wider themes such as pollution in rivers and seas, the effects of acid rain or the partial destruction of the ozone layer.

Ideas for Action

- Form your own 'Greenspace' group (for boys and girls!).
- Conduct your own litter survey. Find out where most of the litter is deposited:
  (a) in school.
  (b) in your area.

  Follow up work might include the following points:
  Are there enough litter bins provided?
  Where are they placed?
  What types of litter are usually discarded in the street?
  How best can you persuade people not to drop litter?

- Set up collection points in your school for the following items:
  glass bottles
  tin cans made from aluminium
  waste paper

  Ask a parent or teacher to assist with transport, or contact a local firm dealing in waste material who may collect the items for recycling. Details can often be found in local newspapers.

- Encourage the use of recycled paper both at home and at school.

- Conduct a sample survey of one hundred cars. How many use lead free petrol?

- Ask for a room or area to be set aside at school with a notice board and display table where you can place notices, items of interest, information and exhibits. To maintain interest, make sure the material is changed regularly.

- Write to national organizations such as Greenpeace or Friends of the Earth requesting further information. (Addresses are given on page 79.)

Discuss   Why would it be dangerous for young children to play in this area?

              Why do you think some people dump this type of rubbish in the countryside?

Read   **Why Should We Bother?**

              'Now more than ever the Earth needs all the friends it can get.'

              This is the simple message from one organization called Friends of the Earth.

What is **Friends of the Earth**?

Friends of the Earth is an organization that works to improve the environment. We do this by trying talking to governments, the people who run factories and industry, and anybody else who can help. We try to persuade them to protect the environment.

Friends of the Earth campaign in many areas. These include the destruction of the world's tropical rainforests, water pollution, air pollution, waste and recycling, the use of energy, countryside and agriculture and transport.

Local Groups

In Britain, Friends of the Earth have over 180,000 supporters and 280 local groups. These groups campaign, all over the country, for a better environment. Many also deal with problems that occur in just one part of the country. Some have been involved in major schemes such as Recycling City in Sheffield.

Friends of the Earth International organize a worldwide network of environmental groups. We have groups in over 30 countries and are active in helping local people all over the world to solve environmental problems.

Friends of the Earth have had a lot of success. We were one of the first groups to let people know about the problems of acid rain. Friends of the Earth's campaign on ozone depletion largely led to the manufacturers removing CFCs from household aerosols. We have done a lot to bring about an improvement to drinking water quality in Britain. Now the work of Friends of the Earth has become even more urgent than ever because of major threats to the environment such as global warming.

Earth Action

Now more than ever the Earth needs all the friends it can get.

If you wish to become involved in the environment and learn more at the same time you could join the Friends of the Earth youth group, Earth Action. There are Earth Action groups all over the country. By joining Earth Action you could meet a lot of other young people who are concerned about the environment. So if you are interested please write and let us know.

There are, of course, many other groups equally concerned about what is happening to our planet. If you are concerned about issues such as acid rain, recycling material, the dumping of poisonous waste, the pollution of our seas and rivers, the destruction of the rain forests and the conservation of wildlife, then write to one of these organizations requesting further information.

Using a Video Camera in School

Notes for Students and Teachers

Many schools these days possess a video camera. However, it is often used only to record the end-of-term concert of school play. The camera operator – usually a keen but inexperienced volunteer – sets up his or her equipment at the back of the hall and points the lens at the stage. The results are often disappointing. The hall is too dark, the sound inaudible, heads in the audience frequently block the stage and most of the action is missed. For this reason, the video camera is under-used and its potential not fully exploited. The aim should be to get the very best out of your camera, but how can you do this?

Using a video camera. Start by shooting a very short scene – and don't forget to practise with the controls first!

Starting Out

It is best to familiarize yourself with the basic operation of the camera before you think about filming. Most video cameras are quite simple to operate but do spend some time on your own, practising with the controls beforehand. I once spent twenty-five minutes in class trying to find the right lead for the television monitor, by which time everyone's enthusiasm for a video project had completely evaporated!

Once you have mastered the basics, try something simple to begin with. Short dialogue, such as an interview, is often a good starting point, particularly if the speakers have been given enough time to prepare their material beforehand. When recording, it is always best to allow the camera to run for at least five seconds before and after shots. Once all the interviews have been recorded, you can use the next lesson to analyse the results.

Playbacks

These always provide interesting insights into television techniques. When you first see yourself on the screen you may want to laugh hysterically, but you can also learn a lot from what you have done. Embarrassed, hesitant pauses and deadpan expression will show you exactly how *not to* communicate! By using a video camera, you can learn the sort of communication skills that will be useful for GCSE oral work and, of course, job interviews.

Group Work

Once you think you have mastered the video camera, you might like to try to create your own television commercial in small groups of four to six. This does require careful preparation beforehand. Study a whole range of advertising, to learn how the professionals do it; then take time to prepare your material. Use props, scenery, sound effects, music, and a basic script. When you come to record your commercial, you could try using several different locations. You may well find that you get as much fun from the preparation stage as from the filming itself. It will also give you a valuable insight into advertising techniques and the time it takes to prepare a short television commercial.

The School Play

If you want to record a school play or concert, make sure that you attend rehearsals. It is essential to know what's coming beforehand and so prepare a *camera script*. Talk to the producer and find out when sudden movements occur on stage or when new characters are to be introduced. Once you are familiar with the play and its characters, you can then concentrate on individuals. Position your camera close to the stage and avoid swinging the camera continually from side to side in an effort to fit everybody in. Lots of close-ups and the occasional slow pan will give much better results.

Sound and Lighting

The small multi-directional microphones on video cameras are very good for close-up work, but less reliable at a distance where they tend to pick up lots of unwanted sounds, such as the scraping of chairs on floors. They can also produce an annoying echo if filming takes place in a large, uncarpeted room. Extension microphones can be attached to most cameras which will improve the quality of the sound.

Most video cameras will operate indoors under normal lighting conditions, although a video light can be a very useful asset in some circumstances. The video camera will generally produce a good quality picture if used properly, but it is unfair to compare this with a professional television broadcast, produced by an army of technicians operating a wide range of sophisticated equipment.

An editing suite is a great help when editing a video, but 'crash editing' can still produce good results.

Editing

Most schools do not possess an expensive editing suite and must rely on a method known as *crash editing* in order to eradicate mistakes and discard unwanted material. This simply means using two video recorders connected by video and audio leads and linked to a television monitor. The master tape is placed in the first machine and a blank tape in the second. By pressing the *play* button on video one and monitoring the pictures on the screen, you can then select the material you wish to record. This can be done by using the *record/pause* buttons on the second video. It is not an easy process to begin with, and it calls for careful synchronization of the pause buttons on both machines. However, with practice, results are satisfactory, although VHS tapes do not copy brilliantly and there may be some distortion on sound and vision, particularly if further copies are made.

Footnote: *For professional advice on all aspects of video filming and editing it is best to consult the local audio-visual aids unit. They may be willing to lend out extra equipment to schools.*

Acting for Camera and Preparing the Video Script

Acting for camera requires special qualities. The use of body language is very important, for unlike radio drama, the emphasis is on what is being *seen*, as opposed to what is being *said*. It is important for actors to be able to motivate themselves, for they do not have a live audience to perform to, as in the theatre. The video script writer must also create situations which can be explored visually – in pictures, rather than just in words. The writer *must* see the action clearly in his mind before he or she prepares the script. One way to achieve this is by producing a storyboard beforehand. This is simply a shot-by-shot guide of the action. A brief sketch should illustrate each intended shot. Notes on location, movement of actors and dialogue (if any) can be added later. This method is particularly useful in preparing a short film.

The layout of the final script is very important both for the actors and the camera team. Normally, television scripts begin in the centre of the page. This allows space for the producer to make notes during camera rehearsals. Directions can then be clearly marked by the side of each speaking part.

Locations

It is best to break down the play into a number of clearly defined scenes (marked INT. for internal shots, and EXT. for outside shots) and also to indicate whether the filming is to take place during the day or at night. This may seem obvious but it is important to check each location beforehand. It may be necessary to alter intended movements of characters, or extra lighting may be required for some scenes.

Scenes for filming are always taken out of sequence and filmed in blocks, which saves a great deal of time. For example, all the Apartment scenes in **The Teen Commandments** were filmed in one day. However, if there is a time lapse between scenes in the same location it may be necessary to move or add various props as required. Characters too may also need to change clothes in order to make each scene as authentic as possible.

Film Directions

Directions should be given in capitals, to distinguish them from dialogue, and enclosed in brackets. Props are often used as an integral part of the story: for example, Scene One of **The Teen Commandments** opens with a girl screaming and a boy holding a knife in his hand. The idea is to create an immediate visual impact, without dialogue, that will leave the viewer guessing and, hopefully, anticipating the next scene. This opening scene is very short, in terms of script and directions, but needs a lot of thought beforehand on how best to achieve the intended result.

All directions for the cast must also be clearly marked in the same fashion. Intended movements and reactions should be included here, for they are just as important as the words spoken.

Glossary

Television production has a language of its own. While it is not necessary to understand all the technical 'jargon', it is useful for the writer to be aware of some of the abbreviations used. Not only does this save time but it can encourage the writer to experiment in future scripts.
Some of the common terms used are:

C.U.	Camera close up to show just a face or part of the body on screen.
L.S.	Long shot, figures or objects at a distance.
Pan	Camera moves slowly to either side from one character (or object) to another.
Pull back	Camera pulling back or moving back from character or object.
SFX	Any special sound effect necessary to the script (e.g. car horn, blast outside).
O.S.	Out of shot. Characters heard but not seen on screen.
Voice over	Spoken narrative added to the scene after filming.
Zoom in or out	(On video cameras) the 'zoom' button on the camera allows for close-up or wide-angled shots.
Fade to grey or black	This facility, on some cameras, allows the user to fade out both vision and sound simultaneously at the end of a scene, or to fade in at the beginning of a new one.

Filming 'The Teen Commandments'

To produce a video lasting about thirty minutes – the estimated running time of **The Teen Commandments** – demands the same effort, concentration and commitment found in any stage production. A production team will certainly need at least two weeks preparation time, even before rehearsals begin.

Once locations have been established, equipment tested and the characters have learnt their lines, it is then advisable to allow at least a week for filming. Rushing the scenes will inevitably produce disappointing results. Even a short sequence, lasting about a minute on film, may take over an hour to get right.

It is not just the problem of characters forgetting lines. Unwanted intrusions in the background, such as inquisitive people or unexpected sounds like a car starting up, can ruin a good 'take' and cause a great deal of frustration. In all types of filming, patience is the key word. To produce a full length play on film does require considerable time and effort. One way round this problem is to set aside a number of lessons as preparation and rehearsal time. Ideally, a video production makes a good summer term project, and a sympathetic headteacher may even allow two or three days' filming towards the end of term.

Where this is not possible, sections of the play can be filmed each week and then played back to the class for discussion and analysis. The ideas for improvisation, listed earlier, also provide excellent material for video filming.

Useful Addresses

Friends of the Earth, 26–28 Underwood Street, London N1 7JQ
Greenpeace, 30–31 Islington Green, London N1 8XE

Acknowledgements

Photographs from the play **The Teen Commandments** feature members of
The Creative Drama Group, Sawston Village College, Sawston, Cambridge.

Cast:
Ben	Mark Tunstall
Kyle	Nick Saich
Lavinia	Kerry Jackson
April	Eva Ferguson
Jack	Simon Radford
Melissa	Katie Grimwade

These photographs were taken by Paul Morris.

Many thanks to Alison Blackwell and Sarah French for their work behind the
scenes, to Eva Ferguson for additional script material, and to Mr F. J.
Marven, Warden of Sawston Village College, for his support in this project.

Text from the leaflet on pages 71–2 has been reproduced by kind permission
of Friends of the Earth.

The illustrations are by Sophie Grillet.

The publishers would like to thank the following for permission to reproduce
photographs:

Barnaby's Picture Library p.70; Stuart Boreham p.75; Martyn Chillmaid
p.73; The Environmental Picture Library, Phil Brown p.51, Charlotte
Macpherson p.20; Paul Glendell p.44, p.69; Greenpeace, Morgan p.6; ICCE,
Mark Boulton p.72; Duncan Phillips p.67.

Other plays in this series include:

Across the Barricades   ISBN 0 19 831272 5
Joan Lingard   adapted by David Ian Neville

The Burston School Strike   ISBN 0 19 831274 1
Roy Nevitt

The Demon Headmaster   ISBN 0 19 831270 9
Gillian Cross   adapted by Adrian Flynn

Frankenstein   ISBN 0 19 831267 9
Mary Shelley   adapted by Philip Pullman

Hot Cakes   ISBN 0 19 831273 3
Adrian Flynn

Paper Tigers   ISBN 0 19 831268 7
Steve Barlow and Steve Skidmore

A Question of Courage   ISBN 0 19 831271 7
Marjorie Darke   adapted by Bill Lucas and
Brian Keaney

Tigers on the Prowl   ISBN 0 19 831277 6
Steve Barlow and Steve Skidmore

The Turbulent Term of Tyke Tiler   ISBN 0 19 831269 5
adapted from her own novel by Gene Kemp